# BE Your OWN Muse

## DAILY EXERCISES TO FALL IN LOVE WITH YOUR FEMININITY

# NINA MADSEN

*Special Art Development*

*Be Your Own Muse*

Daily Exercises to Fall in Love with Your Femininity

*Nina Madsen*

Paperback ISBN: 979-12-5553-000-8
support@specialartbooks.com
www.specialartbooks.com

# Table of Contents

# Introduction

Throughout our life, we're subjected to so many messages about who and what we should be, so much so that our authentic selves tend to get drowned out by the noise. From social media to social conditioning, we're often told things like you have to be in a relationship to be happy, surrounded by others to feel fulfilled, seek praise and approval from outside sources, and follow a well-trod path to find contentment.

This book begs to differ.

It's my belief that nearly everything we need in life, from developing particular skills to growing in wisdom and strength, comes from inside us. It's the magic we possess inside that renders us one-of-a-kind. Not only is this a cause for celebration, but it's also totally reassuring. Here's the thing: we don't need to seek out what we already have!

Every person is extraordinary, and a combination of creative play, practical efforts, and self-reflection can unearth this simple, undeniable truth: There is no greater joy—and there is no better gift you can offer the world—than being you, unique, incredible you.

In the following pages, you'll learn the joy of getting to know your genuine self. You'll discover why you should date yourself—and how. You'll see that tending to yourself first will provide you with the vitality you need to take care of others. You'll understand that cultivating self-admiration is far more important than earning praise from others. You'll learn how to befriend yourself, respect yourself, thank yourself, enjoy yourself, and most importantly, *love* yourself. Along the way, you'll build strength, confidence—and reason after reason to rejoice in the beauty of being *you.*

# Part One:
# Love Yourself

# Chapter One

## Be Your Own Muse

> **"** I am my own muse. I am the subject I know best. The subject I want to know better.
>
> —*Frida Kahlo* **"**

If you've ever heard an artist of some kind mention they need a muse, it means they're in need of inspiration, a pump to their creative flow. Sometimes muses are people, but a lot of times they are things, places, or moments. Muses arrive in countless forms: A conversation overheard, a stunning view, a splendid piece of music, a beautiful poem, or even a headline in the news. They stir up our creative juices, arouse expression, and make us feel *alive.* As such, they've

been sung about, written about, painted about—and desired.

But what if the best muse is the one you have inside? You!

People often downplay their own creativity, saying things like, "I'm just not a creative person." Then, they shut down that side of themselves entirely, thinking it's not within them to be creative! But that's wrong. Every one of us, because of our humanhood, has the capacity for creativity, and we can tap into it if we give ourselves a chance and treat ourselves as our own muse!

Consider the life you've lived, the memories you've made, the people you've met, the places you've visited, the relationships you've developed, the homes you've lived in, and everything you've accomplished. All can serve as a superb source of inspiration. No matter your age or experience, you have a story that's waiting to be told—and sometimes in more than words. Time to take a look back at your life and delve into who you are to find out how you can use the powers inside of you to inspire yourself and others.

## Ask

How might a painting of your life look? What colors does it hold; what symbols and images?

.................................................................................................

.................................................................................................

What sort of strength could it provide others?

.................................................................................................

.................................................................................................

How would it guide the rest of your life?

.................................................................................................................

.................................................................................................................

What lessons could it teach to those who see it?

.................................................................................................................

.................................................................................................................

Most of all, how did this story shape who you are today?

.................................................................................................................

.................................................................................................................

## PUT IT INTO PRACTICE

As you reflect on these questions, endeavor to learn more about yourself.

Take a look at who you are and/or your past and select a part of yourself that intrigues you the most but that you least understand.

11

It could be your general curiosity about life, your skill with numbers, your introversion, your love of rock-and-roll, that time you went skydiving even though you hate heights, your aversion to pickles, your desire to become a chef, or your deep love of nature.

- When, and where, did this part of you take root?

  .................................................................................................

  .................................................................................................

- Why?

  .................................................................................................

  .................................................................................................

- Who was present, and where did it take place?

  .................................................................................................

  .................................................................................................

- How is it—or how does it want to be—expressed?

  .................................................................................................

  .................................................................................................

- Why is it an intricate part of who you are, and how does it emphasize your uniqueness?

..................................................................................................

..................................................................................................

Think about it. Write it down.

Additionally, find an object that inspires you. You could attend a crafts fair in your community, or conduct "armchair travel" by perusing Etsy, Minted, Jungalow, Uncommon Goods, Animi Causa, or Viva Terra. However you choose to find your object, take the time to seek it out. Once you find it, place this object in your self-styled sanctuary—a self-love tip we'll delve into later—and use it to remind yourself of your inner muse's powers.

## CREATIVE EXERCISE

Draw a self-portrait that captures not your reflection in the mirror but the aspects of yourself you find the most fascinating. No need to be a brilliant artist—a bad drawing is still using your creativity!

If you're more of a photographer than a sketcher, opt for a selfie instead.

For further inspiration on how bold and innovative you can get with this exercise, check out the self-portraits by the following artists:

- Sarah Lucas
- Cindy Sherman
- Frida Kahlo
- Tamara de Lempicka
- Jarusha Brown

## Conclusion

Muses arrive in many manifestations, but the most riveting is the one you possess within. Remember that you are your own sense of wonder. Dig deep to find out the why behind who you are and what makes you special. You also don't have to be a photographer or a painter, a writer or a dancer, to express your authenticity. You simply listen, and "get out" what's been revealed to you.

# Chapter Two

## Be Your Own Listening Ear

> "
> Nothing sounds as good to
> the soul as the truth.
> —*Martha Beck*
> "

As women, we often take on a lot, and we often have many people depending on us. We lend a listening ear to our partners and siblings, friends, children, and colleagues. We offer empathy and advice as well as our time and thoughts and energy.

Yet how often do we pause long enough to listen to ourselves? We feel pressured to let our attention to ourselves fall by the wayside, and while others are helped by this, perhaps, we suffer.

As women, we want to connect with others and share our lives. It's a part of our DNA. But while we enjoy that connection and wish to help people we love, at the same time, we want someone to be our listening ear. That may already be a part of your life, but why not start being a listening ear to yourself?

A great deal of clarity comes when you get quiet with yourself while simultaneously shushing your internal critic. Away from the noise of others, you can tend to and befriend your anxieties, understand what your emotions are trying to tell you, reestablish your connection with your intuition, and come to decisions, both minor and significant, based on your own wisdom. Doesn't it sound great?

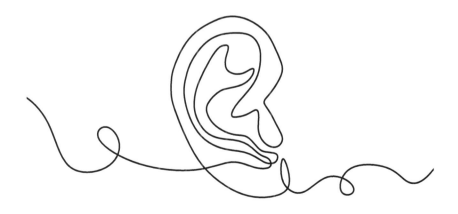

What's more, listening to yourself reveals your core beliefs—both those that are working for and against you. When you come across deeply-seated beliefs that are limiting you, you can make necessary changes. By listening to yourself, you'll also be able to predict how you'll feel in any given situation—and knowing in advance can help you prepare for what awaits.

## PUT IT INTO PRACTICE

Consider an issue that's been bothering you lately—maybe it's an argument with a loved one, a perplexing issue at work, or a major decision about your career.

Carve out time in your day and sit in silence with this concern. Ensure you're in a place that makes you feel comfortable, safe, and nurtured. This may be your bedroom, your favorite bench in the nearby park, a pew at your church, or a gazebo. Bring a notebook and pen with you, in case you want to write down anything or reflect. Remember, this is a wonderful way to get clarity on a situation.

Take several deep breaths to ground yourself. Feel your body anchoring you to the earth. Let the voices of others—your friends, your colleagues, your boss,

your parents—fade away. If they come back, focus on your breath so that it, along with your heartbeat and the organic sounds of your environment, is all that you hear.

Once you're quiet, ask yourself:

- What is bothering me?

  ............................................................................................................

  ............................................................................................................

- What are the pros and cons of the solutions I've been given by others or have considered myself?

  ............................................................................................................

  ............................................................................................................

- What do I genuinely want?

  ............................................................................................................

  ............................................................................................................

- What do I truly think will make a wise decision?

  ........................................................................................

  ........................................................................................

- What do I need?

  ........................................................................................

  ........................................................................................

- Imagine the wisest, most compassionate person in your life responding to your feelings and worries.

  ........................................................................................

  ........................................................................................

- How would they reply?

  ........................................................................................

  ........................................................................................

- How would they reassure you?

  ........................................................................................

  ........................................................................................

- What perspectives would they encourage you to see?

  .................................................................................

  .................................................................................

- What self-negating views would they urge you to get rid of?

  .................................................................................

  .................................................................................

- What solutions would they provide?

  .................................................................................

  .................................................................................

Open a gentle and sympathetic dialogue with yourself—either internally or in your notebook. It will help you gain empathy and insight.

## CREATIVE EXERCISE

Draw an image of a wave using only outlines. Then, take some time to color it in however you like. Reflect on this wave and what it means to you.

Remember the ebb and flow of life. The poet and scholar Rumi taught that no feeling is final. Life is like its own strange sea, and we're floating on it, feeling the movements of the waves underneath us. Sometimes the waves are bigger than others, and sometimes the sea is calm. Reflect on this: Like a wave, your anxiety, bad feelings, and difficulty will pass. Another may come to take its place, but remember there are times of smooth sailing.

## Conclusion

Your own wisdom was likely hard-earned—and it's priceless. Listen to yourself, away from distractions, and it will help you reconnect with yourself in a way you never have before.

# Chapter Three

## Be Your Own Wise, Loving Parent

> " Above all, be the heroine of your
> life, not the victim.
> —*Nora Ephron* "

The busyness of life can prevent us from taking care of ourselves. As I mentioned before, women often let so much else get in the way before we take time for ourselves.

Work, social obligations, household responsibilities, children, relationships, evenings out with friends, and challenging events—all can steer us away from health and wellness. We may lose sleep, eat a less-than-stellar diet, or ditch our commitment to working out.

So many of us stop asking for comfort and a listening ear and forget to just kick back and *rest.*

Maslow's Hierarchy of Needs reveals that in order to ascend to our highest potential, we must first make sure our essential requirements are fulfilled. These are nourishment, sleep, hydration, connection, and shelter. Once we have all of those basics, we can begin to move into the more nuanced challenges of interpersonal relationships, career progress, and achieving our life's purpose.

This is where you as a wise, loving parent to yourself come in. This 'person' exists in all of us—sometimes as a whisper, and sometimes as a shout. Think of this figure as that person on your shoulder, guiding you in the right direction.

That voice tells us when we need to say goodbye at a party, no matter how much fun we may be having, to make sure we get enough sleep that night to get through the next day at work. It warns us of potential danger, reminds us to opt for the apple instead of the cupcake, and might even urge us to indulge in a hot bath when we're overwhelmed and anxious.

Your duty is to reacquaint yourself with this parent inside you. Likely, it's been hidden away because the stress of life distracted you or the needs of others took over your own.

## PUT IT INTO PRACTICE

Examine your life and pinpoint what basic aspects require more attention.

- Do you need more or better sleep?

.................................................................................................................

.................................................................................................................

- Do you need to eat healthier?

  ........................................................................................................

  ........................................................................................................

- Have you been skimping on your vegetables?

  ........................................................................................................

  ........................................................................................................

- Have you been remembering to take your vitamins?

  ........................................................................................................

  ........................................................................................................

- Have you been to the doctor recently?

  ........................................................................................................

  ........................................................................................................

- Are you being easy on yourself, and letting your mistakes teach you rather than get you down?

  ........................................................................................................

  ........................................................................................................

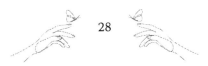

- Do you need more laughter in your life?

  .................................................................................................

  .................................................................................................

- More time with friends?

  .................................................................................................

  .................................................................................................

- Do you need to go out for a walk to clear your head?

  .................................................................................................

  .................................................................................................

Listen to the wise, loving parent you have inside and do as they suggest. Who knows, your inner guide may leave you shocked with a bolt of wisdom.

## CREATIVE EXERCISE

Picture yourself at your healthiest and most vibrant. What would you be doing? Would you be running, swimming, or simply smiling? How would you feel? What would you look like?

Need inspiration? Search through the photos on your phone or an album for a picture of yourself when you looked—and felt—well-rested, at ease, nourished, and happy.

One way to do this is to sketch it, but you could also lay back, close your eyes, and just picture it in your mind. You're still using your unique creativity even if you don't pick up a pencil!

# Conclusion

Self-care is central to your mental, physical, and psychological health. Life is meant to be lived and enjoyed, not just slogged through. Learning to take care of yourself like a parent would along the way will only bring you greater contentment and happiness and respect for who you are.

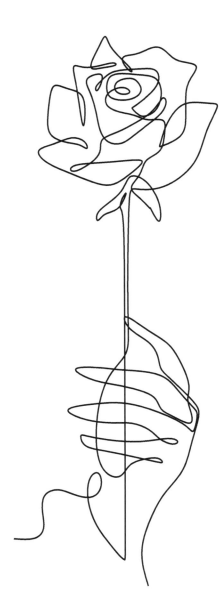

# Chapter Four

## Be Your Own Date

> "
> My mother told me to be a lady. And
> for her, that meant be your own person,
> be independent.
>
> —*Ruth Bader Ginsburg*
> "

The company of others is certainly enjoyable, but the company of yourself can be downright relaxing and pleasant. When you spend quality time with yourself, you stand to learn plenty about the real you. That includes your food preferences, the time of day when you feel most vibrant, even the speed at which you like to walk. It gives you ample opportunities to explore activities, foods, and environments that are new to you, and come to a conclusion based not on others' opinions but rather by listening to your heart.

On your own, you can be whoever you want to be. While that's freeing, often people shy away from being alone because they're afraid to face what's there. Maybe there are things you don't like about yourself, and you don't want to think about them or deal with them. Maybe the negative voice in your head grows stronger when you're alone. But that's what we need to do sometimes. Be alone to remember who we are and what we have to give to the world.

Even if starting off dating yourself sounds scary, I promise it'll get easier the more you do it. In this freeing alone time, you can work through the difficulties that have been holding you back. You can learn to love the way your body looks, stop stressing about your bank accounts, and even forgive yourself for something you have been unable to for a long time. That's because this alone time, which is so rare, gives you the chance to actually be with yourself and hear the strong, passionate voice inside you that's been screaming to be heard. Be alone and begin to let go of all the garbage and love yourself.

## PUT IT INTO PRACTICE

Select a place or activity that excites you—a chic restaurant that recently opened in your town, a unique event that most people in your social circle wouldn't choose for an evening but that holds special meaning for you, or just a film you've been eager to see.

- Schedule it into your calendar—and attend it solo.

- Prepare for it as you would any date by choosing a fun outfit and putting the most cheerful side of yourself into action.

- Throughout your date, pause to notice how you feel, particularly if you're experimenting with a new food or activity, as anything that tears us out of our comfort zone is ripe for self-revelation.

- Once you're home, write in your journal—not only about what you did but also what you took from the excursion. How would you do things differently next time? What are you eager to try next?

- Incorporate solo dates into your schedule to the point that they become second nature—or, perhaps, inspire you to take a bigger leap and travel somewhere exotic without a companion.

## CREATIVE EXERCISE

Think about the setting for your perfect date. Draw it or create a list.

It could be a sunset on a beach, a candlelit restaurant, a drive-in movie theater, sitting by a waterfall. It could be walking through the park with your dog or even pouring a glass of wine for yourself and sitting on your back porch.

It could involve a range of activities or a single memorable event. Envision yourself in this setting alone, and feel how content you are to do exactly as you'd like within this space. Get yourself in the mindset before you head out to do it on your own (especially if it's your first time).

# Conclusion

Becoming content with your own company can be as eye-opening and thrilling as falling in love with another person. It can help create a fresh understanding of who you really are. Besides, if you don't enjoy your own company, how can anyone else?

# Part Two: Love Your Space

# Chapter Five

## Be Your Own Personal Chef

> " A woman is the full circle. Within her is the power to create, nurture, and transform.
> —*Diane Mariechild* "

Left to our own devices most of us working women with kids think there's no reason to make a big deal out of eating when we're dining solo. Often, we call a bowl of cold cereal or a take-out salad perfectly acceptable when no other family members are at home. Or, we may not eat any whole foods at all and simply graze on a combination of random mismatched leftovers.

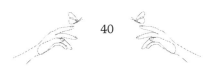

While there's no right or wrong, learning to cook for yourself, and to do so leisurely, boosts self-esteem and self-respect. Indeed, being your own personal chef offers a host of benefits. Cooking is a wonderfully sensuous experience, brimming with tastes and smells and sights that can evoke a tremendous amount of happiness.

And nurturing yourself with delicious eats that are full of essential vitamins and minerals? Always a good idea. (Just ask your wise, loving parent!)

## PUT IT INTO PRACTICE

Start getting excited about it! If you're not usually a cook, do things that will help draw you to the kitchen. Maybe you need to restock on the tools there. Find pots and mixing spoons you like, for example. Make your kitchen a pretty place, and a place you want to be, and you might find yourself enjoying cooking there more and more often. Start small; it doesn't even have to be a copper pot that costs half your savings. I find a sturdy mixing spoon that feels good in my hand makes me want to cook more often!

Another way to get excited is to visit your local farmers' market and purchase fresh, seasonal produce and other foods that either interest or are bound to bring you pleasure. Study up on recommendations for the best way to cook and serve new foods you might not have tried before. And if you don't have money to buy a whole new stock of vegetables, then start with one different kind. If you always reach for carrots, try parsnips. Don't get red beets, hold out for tender golden ones when fall rolls around.

Scour the internet or your grandmother's cookbook for new recipes, and dedicate an evening to creating a meal for yourself. Clear your schedule for time in the kitchen so that you're not rushing through the endeavor. Like a meal cooked with love, this experience should definitely be savored!

As you cook, put on a playlist or podcast you love, and pause throughout to absorb the joys of the experience. Note the tastes and aromas of the items you're preparing, and if it resonates with you, say an internal thanks to the people and our planet, all of whom make such food available.

When you're ready to eat, find a nice quiet spot that's just for you. Make it comfortable and enjoyable. And do whatever you like while you eat; it's all about you. The thoughtfulness you show yourself in this moment can lead to enhanced self-worth—and serve as a reminder that you deserve care, craft, and elegance.

## CREATIVE EXERCISE

Something creative I often enjoy doing is dreaming up a recipe that I might not have cooked before. I like to experiment with what I've already got at home and see if I can make something delicious. This both uses your creative side, and it gives you the chance to make mealtime into something more—a chance to honor yourself.

43

# Conclusion

Cooking for yourself is just another aspect of beautiful self-care that you deserve. Enjoy your adventures with yourself in the kitchen and beyond.

# Chapter Six

## Be Your Own Lover

> " You carry the passport to your own happiness.
>
> —*Diane von Furstenberg* "

Enormous pleasure can be found with loving someone else, but learning to give yourself affection will strengthen your independence and promote self-admiration. And we could all use some of that. But in reality, it can be difficult to know how to love yourself in this way. How can you look at yourself in the way a lover would?

Ask yourself a few questions. How would your lover ideally treat you? Would they offer you compliments?

Rub your feet? Offer to call in take-out for you, or put on your favorite romantic comedy? Would they bring you flowers, love the quirks that make you *you*, and massage your back until you fall asleep?

With the exception of that last part, you are free and able to do all of these things for yourself. In doing so, you can explore your own resilience and your worthiness of love and tenderness. We can all use a little tender loving care at times, and while we can get quite good at giving it to others, too often we forget about ourselves.

## PUT IT INTO PRACTICE

Imagine an activity that engages one of your five primary senses: a massage, a gourmet dessert, a bath, an art gallery, dancing—you name it. Be boundless with your ideas. Incorporate it into your life for a sensuous, solo experience.

Keep in mind, though, that being your own lover doesn't need to be an expense like purchasing a great-smelling perfume or indulging in a slice of tiramisu. You can flood yourself with affection on a daily basis with:

- Self-massage
- Caressing your hair
- Using a wonderfully-scented oil or lotion on your skin
- Telling yourself how you appreciate yourself
- Experimenting with a nourishing skin treatment
- Giving yourself a hug
- Focusing on a project that brings you plea-sure—reading a novel, playing Wordle, paint-ing a picture
- Creating a relaxing bedtime ritual
- Stretching when you rise in the morning and spending the first few moments of your day reviewing how you feel and what you hope to accomplish
- Keeping an ongoing gratitude list of what you adore about yourself and the strides you've made
- Listening to guided meditations
- Using a soft foam roller to get the "kinks" out of your body
- Journaling
- Accepting the errors you've made in the past and using these missteps as a way forward

- Validating your thoughts and feelings, and meeting them with loving responses

## CREATIVE EXERCISE

Draw your favorite dessert—an ice cream sundae, a piece of cheesecake, a square of tiramisu. Imagine the pleasure of biting into it. Return to it when you need a reminder that joy is yours for the taking. Sometimes, we just need to think about our own pleasure!

# Conclusion

Offering yourself affection is empowering, and it also makes you *shine*. Treat yourself with the affection of a lover and watch as your happiness and confidence soar.

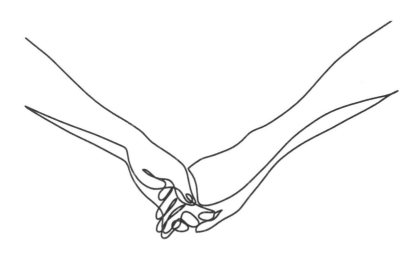

# Chapter Seven

## Be Your Own Source of Light

> "Courage starts with showing up and letting ourselves be seen.
> —*Brene Brown*

We often look to others for qualities we already have inside of us. In getting to know yourself better, you'll discover that the energy you crave—the light you desire—requires nothing more than igniting the flame you carry inside of you. Be your own source of light as you continue your own journey through life.

Being your own source of light is about having the courage to show your true self to others. It's about having the energy, zest, and confidence for life coming from within you, instead of depending on others or external circumstances to get you through the hard times.

Each of the activities in this book is designed to spur this, but you can also do so in a literal way. That means getting outside and flexing your artistic muscles.

## PUT IT INTO PRACTICE

To get you in that light-focused mindset, consider your favorite light or time of day. Is it a soft, subtly-colored sunrise? A vivid sunset? A cozy, rainy afternoon? Why is this your favorite source of light? What does it say about you?

Need some direction? Here are some things to consider:

- Sunrise can signify a cheerful nature. You tend to be upbeat, with a positive outlook on life.

- Dusk may represent a serene personality. You may go with the flow and are often described as fluid.

- Sunset can symbolize a fiery character; someone who tends toward adventure and an active lifestyle.

- Midnight may reveal a quiet, mysterious personality, and a deep, intellectual interest in the universe.

Whatever yours may be, take a self-portrait with your phone camera to capture yourself in this setting. Play with the poses and angles. Look at this photo when you need a reminder that you are lit from within.

## CREATIVE EXERCISE

Using colored pencils, pens, or crayons, create a sky filled with the hues you feel describe you best. Or you can simply buy colored paper of your favorite calming colors or colors which are tied to you. Cut them into squares. Keep them with you to remind you of the light you hold within yourself.

# Conclusion

Being your own source of light means being your best resource, friend, and wellspring of energy. Pull your energy and your zest from within and shine a path forward into a brilliant future.

# Chapter Eight

## Be Your Own Teacher's Pet

> **"** The ability to learn is the most important quality a leader can have.
> —*Padmasree Warrior* **"**

Learning shouldn't cease the moment you finish school and earn that degree. Indeed, study after study shows that continuous learning is the key to happiness and a long life. It also combats boredom and stagnancy. When you extend your education, you develop skills for future opportunities, help maintain a healthy brain, and spark new ideas.

You can pick which topics you'd like to study, and what skills you would like to learn. Perhaps you majored in Mathematics but always loved Botany? Now is the time to get back out on the soil and dig into it (pun intended).

In our modern era, your options are essentially limitless. MasterClass, for example, offers online courses in a variety of fields from screenwriting and personal branding, modern vegetarian cooking to interior decorating. Classes are taught by veritable masters such as Joyce Carol Oates and Carlos Santana. If that's not in your price range, you could check out the free courses provided by your local community center or even a nearby university. There are lots online too!

Build knowledge in something you're interested in, not necessarily something that will help you in your profession or serve your family. The decision to garner new knowledge will fill you with a sense of accomplishment while also keeping your mind active and delighted. Not only that, but learning more can connect you with new people in your interest area. These could be people you meet in a new class, or they could be people you meet and find out who share the same interests as you. These kinds of connections will also build your confidence as you branch out into new worlds.

## PUT IT INTO PRACTICE

Make a list of five subjects that interest you. Whether it's photography, music, or Spanish, go enlist in a local or online class that will teach you one or more of these skills. Prefer to deepen your knowledge on a subject you already know? Consider enrolling in a post-graduate program for no reason other than you're *interested*. Or even head to the local library and take the time to pull out books only on subjects you love!

## CREATIVE EXERCISE

It can be pretty scary to return to education after a long time away, or to start if you've never gone through higher education. In order to deal with the nervousness and fear that comes with this, do a journaling exercise to help you move through it. Continuing education can help you broaden your horizons and expand your life, so you want to do it, but fear might be holding you back!

Take a look at a few of these journaling prompts (Jensen n.d.) to get started:

- What's the worst that could happen?

  ...................................................................................................

  ...................................................................................................

- What exactly about continuing education am I afraid of?

  ...................................................................................................

  ...................................................................................................

- Where do I think this fear comes from?

  ........................................................................................................

  ........................................................................................................

- How would I feel if I knew the outcome was going to be a positive one?

  ........................................................................................................

  ........................................................................................................

## Conclusion

Learning is a pleasure, and it's also an essential part of personal progress. Grow in knowledge as well as self-confidence and security by taking that first step towards advancing your education in whatever way pleases you!

# Chapter Nine

## Be Your Own Handyman

> " Growth and comfort do not coexist.
> —*Ginni Rometty* "

Do you admire self-sufficiency in others? How wonderful would it be if you could grow that skill in yourself? Whether you live alone or with a busy family, know how to fix things in your home. That leaky faucet or the broken shelf you've put off forever can be unique opportunities. Take those challenges on yourself and strengthen your faith in yourself as a reliable resource, while also saving yourself some money. What's more, it provides you with a tangible manifestation of your efforts. It's extremely satisfying to see progress when we put time into something!

This may not be everyone's cup of tea, but just giving it a try can really teach you something about yourself. If you fix something in your house successfully, it can give you fresh confidence and the knowledge that you can depend on yourself. Sometimes, we need to hear that and *see* it.

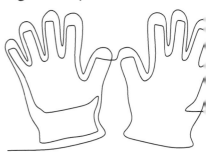

## Put It Into Practice

Learn how to be your own handyman. No need to depend on others! Create a toolkit, complete with a hammer, nails, electric screwdriver, and so on and so forth, and read how-to guides. You can also refer to online videos for step-by-step tutorials to help you make small fixes around your home when needed.

## Creative Exercise

One way to get started on this is to start small. Seek out things you might be able to try to fix yourself – maybe don't start with a broken toilet. Maybe you have a dresser you've always wanted to paint a different color. Painting is a bit easier than getting to the down and dirty of fixing something. Learn about what you

need to do, find the colors you want, and voila! You've got a great project that's all your own. And it gives you the confidence to go for harder, more intricate projects down the line.

## Conclusion

Understanding how your home operates—and having the tools you need to make minor repairs—will strengthen your belief in yourself. You can do this. All you need is the right project.

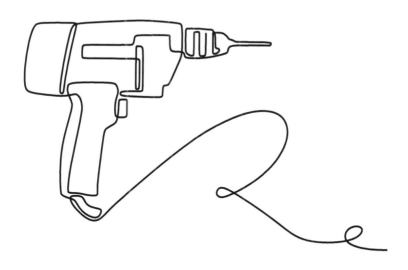

# Part Three: Love Your Company

# Chapter Ten

## Be Your Own Money Manager

> " Make a pact to be in it with yourself for the long haul, as your own supportive friend at every step along the way.
>
> —*Tara Mohr* "

Loving yourself doesn't just make life more enjoyable— acts of self-care also prevent illness and injury. But one element of self-care that's often ignored?

Taking care of your money.

The reason this topic is often left on the shelf is because there are a lot of emotions that surround money. We get these from our parents or the situations in

which we found ourselves growing up. Our own past experiences with money affect how we handle money in the present. And it isn't always good.

Take your feelings surrounding money out of the equation. The abundance or lack of it, or the desire to make more of it doesn't matter. Here's the truth; money is neither good nor evil, but a fact of life. You need to gain control over it so your money can provide you with a sense of order, accomplishment, and control.

When you conquer your financial fears you unlock a new form of empowerment. Once your money is properly managed, you're free to take greater pleasure in relishing life and getting to know yourself on a deeper, more loving level. You'll also be able to afford the necessities that contribute to a long, vibrant life, from purchasing healthy foods to prioritizing your health over your budget.

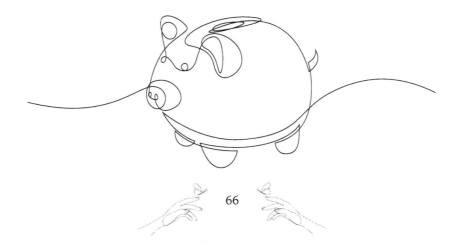

## PUT IT INTO PRACTICE

Establish your financial standing by listing your cash flow, bills, spending, debts, and investments. Determine what you can do to make sure you'll have a financially stable or financially *flourishing* future.

........................................................................................................

........................................................................................................

........................................................................................................

........................................................................................................

## CREATIVE EXERCISE

I know money doesn't always lend itself to creativity. In fact, it makes some people downright nervous. But you can get creative by dreaming about things you envision in your future. Things you might want or need. Sit back, relax, and let your mind soar with ideas.

Then, create a vision board about all the things you might like to buy or services you'd want to be able to purchase in the future. Maybe it's a trip to Spain

or a new pair of running shoes you've been eyeing up lately. Whatever it is, a vision board can help you "keep your eye on the prize" and motivate you to achieving that money-earning goal!

Another exercise you might enjoy is keeping a spending journal. It's not just to keep track of your finances, but what people spend money on shows them a lot about themselves. For example, you might have spent sixty dollars on a night out with friends, but then you only spent ten dollars on yourself to go on your "self-date". What does that say?

## Conclusion

Finances are frequently missing from the self-care conversation, but possessing enough money to pay your bills, engage in pleasurable activities, save for emergencies and the future, and make large purchases—gives you a sense of security as well as control over your life

# Chapter Eleven

## Be Your Own Booking Agent

> " Talk to yourself like you would to someone you love.
>
> —*Brene Brown* "

Agents who help authors, athletes, and actors have nailed the skill of advocating for others. They know their clients well and have no qualms about touting their talents and accomplishments. In fact, it's a vital part of their job description.

As splendid as it may be to hear someone else boast about your skills, keep in mind that you have this power too. And while you don't have to announce it over the phone to a litany of people who may or may

not hire you, knowing and owning your gifts will give you the strength to power through difficult situations, nail a job interview, date with confidence, try new endeavors, and ultimately, hold your head high.

## Put It Into Practice

Write down a list of five things about yourself that are remarkable. This could take some time, especially if you're not used to thinking about yourself this way. Don't worry. Take all the time you need.

.......................................................................................................

.......................................................................................................

.......................................................................................................

.......................................................................................................

.......................................................................................................

Your skills could be your pitch-perfect singing voice, your green thumb, your ability to remember birthdays, your love of historical fiction, your unique understanding of animals, or anything that stands out to you as unique.

Need inspiration?

Recall compliments you've received, testimonials from clients, the words your closest friends use to describe you, or even positive messages others have written about you on social media. Boil down these compliments into a list of traits or skills.

.................................................................................................

.................................................................................................

.................................................................................................

.................................................................................................

.................................................................................................

Next to each item, list the ways that you use this talent. If it's underused, imagine how you might make better use of it? How can you showcase it more often, and use it in a positive way that others enjoy?

Keep this list somewhere special, and refer back to it when you need to remember your amazingness. And no one is free from greatness. We all have it!

# CREATIVE EXERCISE

Sketch pictures of each of the five qualities you've identified.

It could be a music symbol to represent your voice, a plant to demonstrate your gardening skills, a birthday candle to symbolize your memory, a book to show your passion, or an animal you adore.

Be as creative or as straightforward as you please. These images represent the contributions you have to give! Don't hide them away. Keep them in view, so you are always reminded of your unique attributes. Display these sketches in a place where you'll see them every day. Feel free to update them when you discover new sides to yourself.

# Conclusion

We all need to have somebody who's got our back. Stop waiting around for someone to do it for you. You have everything you need to have your own back and support yourself in whatever you want to do.

# Chapter Twelve

## Be Your Own Support System

> 66
>
> I am mine, before anyone else's.
>
> —*Nayyirah Waheed*
>
> 99

Having a friend or family member to call upon during times of distress helps in countless ways. They can hold you, counsel you, reassure you, or simply listen. The best of them will know the perfect moment to hand over a tissue, get you out of a bad situation, and exactly what flavor to get when they want to share a pint of ice cream with you. As humans, we need other people, especially during those rough times which come to us all. It's important to have people in your life who act as your support system.

At the same time, acting as your own best friend, closest confidante, and support system serves as a reminder that you're capable of handling life's curveballs. Build up your strength in supporting yourself and you will marvel at what you can handle. While we do need people, and people add so much to our lives, we don't need them for everything. For instance, we don't need people to tell us we can support ourselves and get through difficult times.

A bad day, a bad month, a bad year, none of it matters. All of that and more can be managed with a huge dose of self-love, understanding, and a few comforting treats. Remember, you're your own ally. At the end of the day, it's you with yourself, and you want to be able to depend on yourself.

## PUT IT INTO PRACTICE

Create a tangible "support system" toolkit you can unearth whenever you're having a bad day.

Include a box of tissues, a loving note of encouragement to yourself, a bar of dark chocolate, a sweet-smelling candle, a beloved book or photo, a journal to jot down your thoughts and feelings, and

a list of songs and movies that will give you comfort. Fill a mini notebook full of self-affirmations that you know will help pull you out of a spiral and add it to the toolkit. Just like having a safe space to run away to, this toolkit can give you the right kind of boost you need to support yourself during stressful times.

## CREATIVE EXERCISE

Write a letter to your past self when you were going through something tough. Encourage your past self, and explain how you go through it. When you have a tough time again, you can always turn back to this letter and realize how you supported and guided yourself.

........................................................................................................

........................................................................................................

........................................................................................................

........................................................................................................

........................................................................................................

# Conclusion

There are moments in life when your greatest comfort is yourself. It gives you confidence and strength as well to know that you can depend upon yourself, and that you're able to get through those tough times. Having other people is great, but don't forget the support system that is beautiful, wonderful you!

# Chapter Thirteen

## Be Your Own Coach

> " Everything you need is already inside you.
>
> —*Elena Sonnino* "

Personal trainers, life coaches, that friend who persuades you to always give it your all—these contacts, as well as others, can help elevate you. They push you to new heights and remind you of your greatness. They keep you going even when you feel like you don't have anything else to give.

The secret is that, even if you don't think it, you're completely capable. So much of what you accomplish physically or mentally hinges on your mental state. With the right one, you'll see a myriad things that you can do with or without support. You are an amazing

individual. By using uplifting words, you too, can evoke the coach inside of you. With regular practice, you'll feel a stronger bond with yourself and a deep well of self-confidence. This is another way you can be your own support system, only this time, you're acting more like a coach yelling out instructions and guidance as you move through the activity. Tell yourself, "You can do this!" with conviction.

This practice can help you quiet any negative voices which are so often inside our heads telling us we can't do it or that we're not strong enough. A coach would never say that to you, so you shouldn't say it to yourself. Coach yourself with positive affirmations, and you can achieve your goals.

## PUT IT INTO PRACTICE

Select a game or exercise that can be performed solo. It could be yoga or swimming; running or biking. Coach yourself lovingly and encouragingly to meet or exceed your personal best.

- If you enjoy planks, for example, time yourself. The next time you perform this move, aim to hold it for thirty seconds longer.

- If you're an aspiring yogi, find a more vigorous class online or in your area, or add an extra hour to your weekly yoga routine.
- If swimming is your thing, aim to get into the water at least five times per week.
- If mountain biking is your go-to pleasure, find a new, challenging trail.

Throughout the experience, urge yourself to reach your goals with positive affirmations. We can always improve. While that's stressful for some, it's actually what gives life a bit more spice. We can always get better!

## CREATIVE EXERCISE

Create a vision board for something you want to get better at. If it's fitness, create a board that encourages you to keep going even when the going gets tough. You can also build a goal chart to map out your goals as you achieve them (for example, track your plank times and your goals for the exercise).

Record your successes and your growth, and you can actually see changes happening over time. This will encourage you to keep on going, just like a coach would.

# Conclusion

Being your own coach gives you the chance to change the negative voice in your head and provide yourself with positive messages and advice. Let's do the ol' switcheroo!

# Chapter Fourteen

## Be Your Own Stylist

> "Character is your beauty; style is your strength.
> —*Debasish Mridh*"

What constitutes fashion is as subjective as what renders a piece of art remarkable. Chances are, you're drawn to styles that are directly aligned with your personality and lifestyle. Tend towards yoga pants and tennis shoes? You're most likely active. Love to go to secondhand stores for vintage finds? That's your inner treasure hunter calling out to you. Drawn to classic lines? You may feel excited by structure or a sense of strength.

Whatever your preference may be, it's *you*—and that's cause for celebration. Style is a way of announcing yourself to the world and showing, yes, your true colors.

## PUT IT INTO PRACTICE

We all have a power outfit, some ensemble that emboldens us. What makes you feel unstoppable? A pencil skirt and stilettos or a sundress and sandals? Whatever it may be, shop with one objective in mind to find items that will empower you, make you feel good, and make you feel you. Select shoes or

accessories that will elevate the look and give you a boost of confidence.

## CREATIVE EXERCISE

Draw three items of clothing that speak to you. Use the colors you're drawn to most to color them in. Consider the meanings behind these colors and how they can enhance your well-being:

- Red=Passion and Energy
- Yellow=Joy and Optimism
- Orange=Energy and Stimulation
- Aqua=Peace and Clarity
- Brown=Stability and Nature
- Grey=Mystery and Fluidity
- Blue=Trust and Serenity
- Purple=Luxury and Imagination
- Lavender=Love and Grace
- Pink=Warmth and Playfulness
- Green=Harmony and Prosperity
- Black=Strength and Sophistication
- White=Hope and Simplicity

Also, try out the closet challenge. Take a look at the clothing inside your closet and assess what you've got with this new color information in mind. Think about how much of what you own actually reflects who you are and what picture you want to present

to the world. Try your best to go through your closet and get rid of at least five things that don't fit the bill, and replace them with clothing pieces that do have meaning and do reflect who you are.

## Conclusion

Dress for you and you alone. While it's fine to adhere to the latest fashions, think about what you want to wear, what makes you feel good, and what expresses what's really inside you.

# Part Four:
# Love Your Spirit

# Chapter Fifteen

## Be Your Own Dance Partner

> "I do not try to dance better than anyone else. I only try to dance better than myself.
> —*Arianna Huffington*"

Dancing is so many things. It's exercise; it's art; it's self-expression, and it's just downright fun. Whether it's your living room or a ballet studio, dancing enhances self-esteem, bolsters body confidence, and in group settings, helps build social connections. A lot of people find dancing a little stressful, not unlike public speaking, because they feel like it's a show in front of others, or that they have to hit all the right steps to be considered a 'good dancer'.

But dancing doesn't have to be about showing others or getting the steps down. It's one activity that acts like art, and it's an incredible way to enjoy expression without fear of judgment, especially when you dance alone. And that's my challenge to you!

## PUT IT INTO PRACTICE

Don't worry, you don't need to know specific dance moves in order to get something special out of dance. Use a freebie music app or website to find some quality music and create a playlist of your favorite dance songs.

Here are a few to jumpstart your thinking:

- "Roses", by SAINt JHN
- "Dancing Queen", by ABBA
- "Stayin' Alive", by the Bee Gees
- "Just Dance", by Lady Gaga

Clear your furniture, turn down the lights, and dance as if there's no tomorrow. This could be anything from Hip-Hop to Belly Dancing; from African Dance to Ballet.

Keen on learning some new moves? Check out dance tutorials online or join a class in your area. Keep an open mind; you might fall in love with something unexpected like Aerial Dance or Contemporary. Just let yourself go and feel free as you move to the music.

## CREATIVE EXERCISE

Start your playlist and draw the first thing that comes to mind. Perhaps it's a pair of dancing shoes. Maybe it's a martini glass. It might be something wildly imaginative. Whatever it is, use it to inspire you to get up and *shake it.*

Try to dance to one song per day, and then reflect on how you feel afterward, expressing yourself in this physical way. Are you happier? Feel looser, more relaxed? Do what feels good, and maybe you can start to add more songs to your daily dance sessions.

# Conclusion

Weaving dance into your life increases overall happiness, and let's face it: it's a great workout. Start getting your dance moves out every day, and enjoy the inner practice of just letting go.

# Chapter Sixteen:

## Be Your Own Spa Tech

> " Almost everything will work again if you unplug it for a few minutes, including you.
> —*Anne Lamott* "

Spa days are synonymous with self-care for a good reason. These are moments to pamper yourself from head to toe and cultivate self-love, relieve stress, and build tranquility in yourself. The best part? You don't need to slap down a great deal of money to experience the benefits of a spa. You can indulge in a spa day from the comfort of your own home and enhance the entire experience. There's no need to worry about a single thing besides yourself and your own enjoyment.

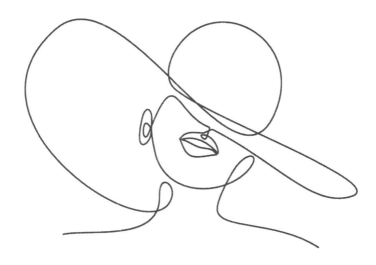

## PUT IT INTO PRACTICE

Treat yourself to a solo spa day within your own space. Check out a few of these ideas:

- Take a long, luxurious bath. Add bath bombs to the water, light a candle, bring a magazine with you, or play soothing music. Before getting out of the tub, wash your hair and apply a DIY deep conditioning treatment.

## Deep Conditioning Treatment

- One ripe avocado, smashed
- One cup of coconut milk
- One tablespoon each of honey and olive oil
- Two drops of Tea Tree Oil

Mix all ingredients together. Apply to hair and let sit for 10-15 minutes before rinsing.

- Create a DIY moisturizing facial with two tablespoons of plain yogurt, one teaspoon of raw honey, and a splash of lemon juice. Follow with a nourishing moisturizer, a lip scrub made with sugar, honey, and olive oil, and a face serum.
- Paint your nails, pluck your eyebrows, and use a scented moisturizer. Relax for a few hours in a bathrobe. These small acts of self-care have enormous results.

## CREATIVE EXERCISE

Try to give yourself a massage from your toes all the way up to your scalp. Feel the strength of your muscles and bones as you engage and connect with yourself. This is pampering at its finest.

# Conclusion

Relaxation is a vital component of a life well-lived. Allow yourself the time and space to indulge in something so wonderful as a 'spa day'. You deserve it.

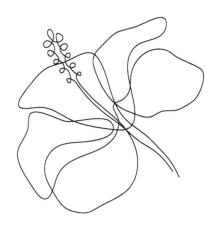

# Chapter Seventeen

## Be Your Own Interior Designer

> "
> Home is the nicest word there is.
> —*Laura Ingalls Wilder*
> "

Possessing a room or space of your own, even if it's one corner of your living room, can give you a place to think, unwind, process your emotions, and feel inspired. We all need our space, a place where we can just be and be ourselves. No one is there to judge us or hurt us. No one is there to tell you what to do or give you more tasks. This space should be where you can run to when life gets a little bit too much.

Given that it's for you and dedicated to you, your personal space ought to reflect who you are, what you hope to accomplish, and the life you have lived. When spending time in this place, you have time to deepen your self-appreciation, set goals, and think back to fond memories. It's a place where you can give yourself even more love.

## Put It Into Practice

Designate a space within your home to call your own, even if you live alone.

- It could be a corner of your living room, or a vanity set in your bedroom, or a place on your patio or in your yard.
- Select accent pieces, such as a throw pillow, in colors and designs that appeal to you.

- Include small touches that spur relaxation and creativity, such as candles, essential oils, prayer beads—whatever speaks to you. These can be purchased new or used, or swapped with a friend.

- Place meaningful items, such as a figurine you picked up on your travels, or that set of book-ends you received as a gift, in your area.

- Adorn the walls with art, photographs, or quotes that have some meaning to you or evoke a wonderful memory.

- Top it all off with a plant or flower arrangement you love to beautify the space and to remind yourself of the link between tender loving care and growth.

Need more ideas? Check out some decorating blogs or inspiration websites for tips on renovating small spaces. The goal is to create a sanctuary where you can decompress, recharge, gather inspiration, or just be.

## CREATIVE EXERCISE

Sketch your ideal living room, bedroom, bathroom, or kitchen. Focus on the details—from plants to keepsakes—that will make it completely yours. Use colors that resonate with you. Add to this drawing with each new burst of inspiration you receive.

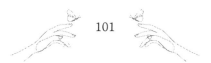

# Conclusion

Joseph Campbell called it a place of "human incubation." Virginia Woolf dubbed it a "room of one's own." You may call it your "She-Shed." Whatever you nickname it, your space is your sanctuary, a place we all need to have to get away and enjoy being ourselves.

# Chapter Eighteen

# Be Your Own Wellspring of Hope

> " Hope and fear cannot occupy the
> same space. Invite one to stay.
> —*Maya Angelou* "

Giving into fear may be a normal human reaction, but there are few better feelings than rising above that fear and crushing it. While friends, family, and mentors can provide you with hope, faith is a flame you should always keep alive in your heart.

Hope is so special that besides love, it's one of the many things musicians sing about, artists paint about, and writers write about. It is such an incredible and powerful human emotion, and it can literally change

a bad situation into one that doesn't look so bad, with light at the end of the tunnel.

With hope comes a way out of a difficult situation, as well as patience. Hope provides a sense of security and gives birth to the imagination. It's a way to keep a light burning even if everything around you feels like darkness. And this can all come from inside *you.*

## PUT IT INTO PRACTICE

Look back upon your life and select three specific times when hope pulled you through. It could be the persistence of pushing past a difficult time in an important relationship, the resilience you found during a moment of grief, or the faith you had in knowing that negative feelings fade. Journal freely about these times, and how they strengthened you.

You always need something to look back on when things start to go south, as they always do! Use these journal entries to remind you of how you were strong and made it through.

## CREATIVE EXERCISE

Select an image that always brings you hope. Don't be afraid to fall back on a standard one like a flower, a peace sign, the infinity symbol, or a lotus. Add words that inspire you to your drawing. This might be a piece you want to frame and hang up to always remind you to keep on hoping.

## Conclusion

Finding hope from within supports resilience and independence. It's how you light a way through tough times. Just like being your own inner light, hope is like a beacon that keeps on shining even when it may seem hopeless.

# Chapter Nineteen

# Be Your Own Voice of Reason

> " A strong woman understands that the gifts such as logic, decisiveness, and strength are just as feminine as intuition and emotional connection.
>
> —*Nancy Rathburn* "

Toxic positivity has shown that aiming for perpetual happiness is not only unrealistic but also dangerous. When you look at the bright side in order to avoid the truth or assume a false happiness, that practice can prevent you from processing your emotions and experiencing true growth. That results in a buildup of pain certain to build up into a horrible, destructive explosion.

And yet the opposite holds true. If you hold on to gloomy thoughts and emotions they can leave you feeling miserable.

One solution to finding the balance within these two extremes is to turn to logic and reason when you're dealing with distressing emotions and self-negating thoughts. Also known as cognitive reframing, this practice challenges you not to look on the bright side, per se, but to view your circumstances from a kinder, more rational perspective. Some people refer to this practice as changing your lens.

Through your new lens, you can keep yourself from falling down the rabbit hole of shame, guilt, anger, regret, and sorrow, and steer yourself closer towards a more secure and stable middle ground.

## PUT IT INTO PRACTICE

When confronted with an uncomfortable thought or distressing emotion, step away from your mind and consider your ideas and feelings from a more objective stance.

- How does this train of thought make you feel?

  ....................................................................................

  ....................................................................................

- How do you feel about these thoughts in general? (i.e. I hate that I beat myself up all the time)

  ....................................................................................

  ....................................................................................

- Write down your answer, then try an approach called Walking the Circle. Jot down three other imagined perspectives on the situation. How else could you look at this problem? What would someone next to you, behind you, or watching from far away see?

  ....................................................................................

  ....................................................................................

- Next, practice what Patanjali termed 'prati-pak-sha-bhavana' in the *Yoga Sutras*: Cultivate the opposite thought. For example, if you make a mistake at work, reframe it as an opportunity. Now how would you tell yourself this story? Write it down and then read it out loud to yourself.

........................................................................................

........................................................................................

## CREATIVE EXERCISE

With your colored pens or pencils, create a rainbow that starts with your most heightened emotion and its corresponding color. Red, for example, to represent rage. Use lighter hues to arrive at the shade, or emotional state, you want to be in.

Here are several ideas:

- Red attracts feelings of excitement and strength
- Blue evokes feelings of competency
- Pink encourages sweeter, kinder notions
- Purple awakens ambition and spirituality
- Orange supports confidence

## Conclusion

Avoid the trap of negativity by approaching your thoughts and emotions from a sound, logical place. We all need the voice of reason now and again. Be that for yourself and learn to look at new perspectives on a tricky situation.

# Chapter Twenty

## Be Your Own Admirer

> ❝ Knowing what you admire in others is a wonderful mirror into your deepest, as yet unborn, self. ❞
>
> —*Gretchen Rubin*

We're used to admiring others. Every time we come upon someone who has a great skill or a wonderful personality, we admire them. It can be so easy to change that admiration into jealousy or compare other people to ourselves. Sometimes admiring others can help you live up to your own potential, which, by the way, is endless. Anytime you stop to admire yourself you reinforce healthy behaviors and enrich your self-confidence. Self-admiration gets rid

of that pesky dissatisfaction which comes from too much comparison.

Admiration of yourself can get a bit of a bad rap. For some, especially those who already struggle with self-confidence, it can feel like you're just being arrogant or thinking you're the greatest. It's not meant to be that way at all! Sure, sometimes people take admiring themselves to a whole new level, but far too many people swing entirely the other way, hardly admiring themselves even when they should.

That's where things turn dangerous. How are you going to achieve your dreams, have wonderful relationships, and get what you want out of life, if you don't first love yourself and admire what you have to offer? We've all got something unique about ourselves, but if you're not sure where to start, pick something small. I'm good at cleaning the kitchen or I always remember to say happy birthday to friends, that sort of thing. Those small, everyday compliments are a great way to do kind things for yourself.

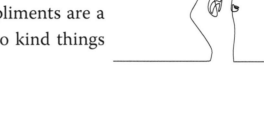

## PUT IT INTO PRACTICE

Treat yourself as a secret admirer would. Buy yourself a bouquet of flowers, or some other token of admiration. Take yourself out, buy yourself some ice cream, or some nice chocolates.

Send yourself a text or email congratulating yourself on a job well done, a handwritten note about an issue you've conquered, or a quality you admire in yourself. Keep it in a place you'll encounter often, whether it's your underwear drawer or in your car's center console.

Thank yourself for being *you* on a regular basis.

## CREATIVE EXERCISE

Select three adjectives to describe your most outstanding characteristics, then write down and draw some illustrations alongside them. (Remember, you're allowed to do a bad drawing!) Why do you feel this way about them? Start to look at yourself through new eyes: the eyes of an admirer.

## Conclusion

Admiration is not a bad thing. It's about taking the time to look at what you've got to contribute to the world! Because everyone's got something. Don't let anyone stop you from appreciating who you are.

# Final Words

There's an enormous amount of beauty and freedom in being you. I know the world tries to tell us a different story, it tries to say that you need to look a certain way, act a certain way, or have certain skills in order to be considered worthy or valuable. Those messages from the world are constant, so it can be very easy to fall into that trap of feeling like you're falling short.

But this book is about reframing your perspective on who you are and what you contribute to the world. It's about fighting against those constant messages from the world that you're lacking and fighting back with the power of self-love.

You are you, a unique individual with abilities and traits like no one else in the world. Why not savor those uniquenesses and go into each day with the self-confidence you deserve to own?

Love yourself and learn more about who you are by being your *own*:

- muse
- listening ear
- wise, loving parent
- date
- personal chef
- lover
- source of light
- teacher's pet
- handyman
- money manager
- booking agent
- support system
- coach
- stylist
- dance partner
- spa tech
- interior designer
- wellspring of hope
- voice of reason
- admirer

Even if not all aspects of these activities appeal to you, you can still learn so much about yourself through playing all these different roles in your own life. Learning more about yourself can help you create a fuller, happier life because you understand why you are the way you are. You understand both your weaknesses and your strengths. But remember to love yourself through them all. You are the only person on this planet who can be you. That realization is truly beautiful, just like you.

*Bonuses*
# OUR GIFTS FOR YOU

Subscribe to our Newsletter and receive these free materials

www.specialartbooks.com/free-materials/

*References*

Instagram: @specialart_books
Facebook Page: Special Art Books
Website: www.specialartbooks.com

# Impressum

For questions, feedback, and suggestions:

support@specialartbooks.com

Nina Madsen, Special Art

Copyright © 2023 Special Art

www.specialartbooks.com

Images by © Shutterstock

Made in the USA
Columbia, SC
10 January 2024